Beautiful Little Girl

I Like Me!

Beautiful Little Girl: I like me!
Copyrighted ©2021 by Ama Oforiwaa Aduonum
Illustrations copyright by Kojo Kisseh Aduonum
ISBN: 9781949109801
Library of Congress Control Number: 2020940710
Printed in the United States
Anchor Book Press, Ltd
440 W. Colfax Street, Unit 1132
Palatine, IL 60078

Beautiful Little Girl

I Like Me!

Written by Ama Oforiwaa Aduonum
Illustrated by Kojo Kisseh Aduonum

Anchor Book Press · Palatine

Dedication

To all girls, everywhere.

Little girl, big girl
Beautiful girls
That's me, that's you
I am beautiful! You are beautiful!
Girls are beautiful

You want to know me
You want to know you
Read about me, read about you
Read about beautiful girls

Little girl, big girl
Beautiful girls
I do Me!
You should do you!

Little girl, big girl
Beautiful girls
I am unique!
So are you

I love math, science, reading
I love history, dance, cooking
I love music too
All subjects

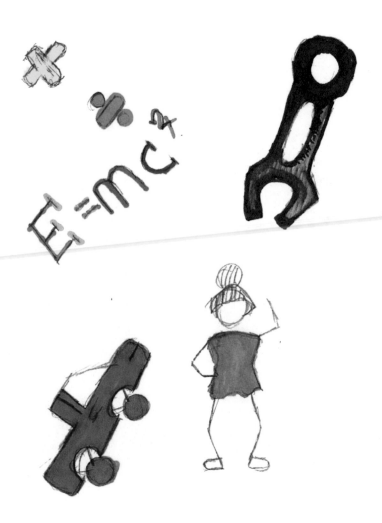

I play with dolls, mud, and sand
I play with trucks, tools, and the band

Check me out on robotics
Hauling rocks, cooking meals, dealing on wheels

I like to work with tools
Create with tools, build with tools,
Construct with tools

I change tires, tie ties
Bake pies and catch flies
I fly high
So can you

Little girl, big girl
Beautiful girls
I am one
You are too

I feel anxious and scared
I get angry and mad
I can be fiery, fierce, and shy
Don't ask why

When I get angry
I scream
I read, I dance, I draw

Or I remain silent and withdraw

They say I am wild, crazy, and bossy
I say I am lively, jaunty, and sassy
I can speak up
I am a leader in the assembly

I rumble and tumble
Like the ocean waves
I roll and fumble
Beneath the hidden caves
Shuffling and scuffling
Along the way

I love yellow, orange, and blue
Green, red and pink. It's true
I see all colors of the rainbow
Have a beautiful hue

Listen up!
I love my eyes
Contacts, glasses, or plain
Thank goodness I have eyes
To see the gentle rain

Elf ears, bear ears, elephant ears
Fish ears, rabbit ears, I have no fears
I can hear, I can hear
Thank goodness I have ears

You say
My nose is flat, pointed, spread all over
I say that is beautiful
I can smell the sweet fragrant aromas
Hmm!!

My lips are thin, cleft, or fat
I don't worry about that
Thank goodness I can eat
Sweet treats
Yumm!

My teeth are gapped, braced, or missing
Thank goodness I can swallow
A marshmallow
Yumm!!

My cheeks are puffed, sunken, flushed
Doesn't bother me
Still a place to plant a kiss

I am fat, skinny, tall, or short
Thank goodness
I have a body to strut
Down the street

Little girl, big girl
Beautiful girls

I am bow-legged or no legs
Knocked knees or square knees
I ride a bike, or I climb the trees
I push my wheels down the street

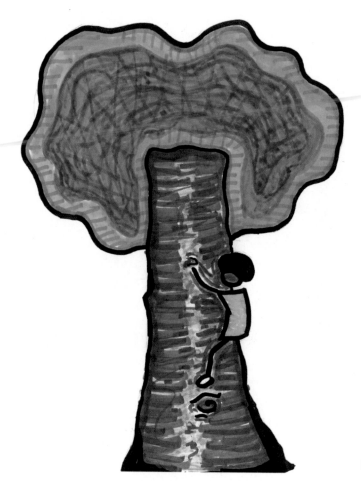

Flat feet, duck feet, itsy-bitsy tiny feet
I walk down the street
I limp down the street
Thank goodness I am alive

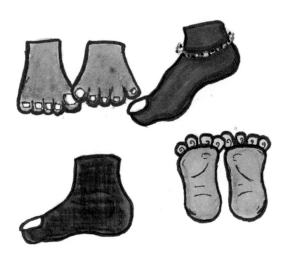

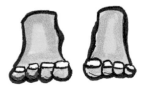

I am alive, I am alive, I am alive
To see the beauty of a world
Alive

I have marks on my face
Pimples, freckles, dimples
You can name them
I cherish them all
My symbols of beauty
You cannot deny

My hair is curly, straight, tightly coiled
Stringy, nappy, dread-locked, bald
Thank goodness
I have a head

My skin wraps the present inside
Brown, white, yellow, black
Oily, dry, and ashy white
Veins, cellulite, and spider webbed
Even a handle on my waist
Beautifully wrapping the gem inside

Clothes, shoes, make-up or not
Do not define me
They adorn the beauty inside

Little girl, big girl
Beautiful girl
I am my girl
You are our girl

Little girl, big girl
Beautiful girl
I am unique!
You are rare
Do not compare

I am wise, smart, and irreplaceable
I am strong-willed and stubborn
But don't get me twisted
I am respectful
Mindful of others
Vulnerable and emotional
I am like no other

I make mistakes
Wrong takes
That's ok
They don't define who I am
I learn from them
That's the key that makes me great!

Whoever says
Girls mustn't do this
Girls can't be that
Doesn't know me
Doesn't know you

I can be an astronaut
A chef, a waitress, or a nanny
I can be a pilot, a teacher, an author, or an artist
I can be what I want to be

A girl can be a president
Or a medical resident
She can be head of state
She shapes her fate

I am a warrior like
Nana Yaa Asantewaa of Asante
Queen Nzinga of Umbundu
Lozen of Apache
Nakano Takeko of Japan
Harriet Tubman or
Sacagawea

Little girl, big girl
Beautiful little girls

Beautiful inside
Beautiful outside

I am one in a million
A rare gem
Specially made to be ...
Me

My Maker made no mistake
I am sufficient
I am enough
I am not a mistake

I am whole
I was made to be me
No one needs to make me complete

Happy to be alone
Happy to be with you
Happy with myself
I can be me when I am with you
Or I can be me alone
I am enough
Flawed yet flawless

I trust me
I know me
I can rely on me
You can rely on you
Gi-rrrrl!
Girls, girls, girls are fun
But don't get us wrong
Girls are strong

Little girl, big girl
Beautiful girls

I am the Sun
That rises every morning
Warms the world
Brightens the Earth
I am my sunshine
BAAMMM!!

I am the rooster that crows
At first morning light
Ko-ku-roo-koooooo!!!!
I am the rooster that crows
Loud and clear

Ko-ku-roo-koooooo!!!!
Wake up world
Girls are here!

I am the rainbow
I bring peace and calm
I am vibrant and flamboyant
My beauty shines throughout the world
I rock
You rock

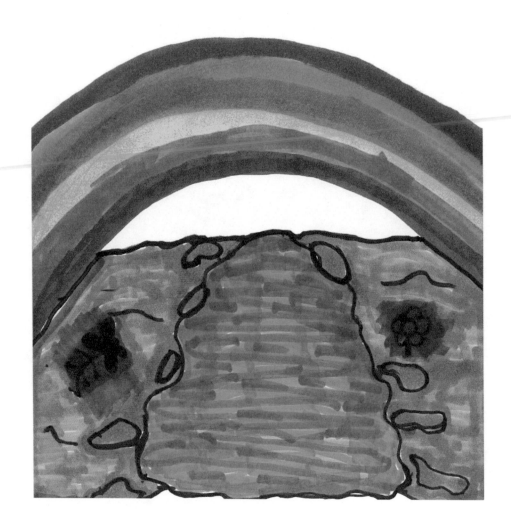

I am a little girl, I am a big girl
A beautiful girl, in my own way
With permission from nobody
I am a beautiful girl

Stop!
Stop, I say!
Do not redefine me
I like who I am
I like how I look
I decide who I am

You may not squash me
My many experiences
Hopes and dreams
They are mine
I define me

Little girl, big girl
Beautiful little girls
Customs created anew
Norms do not define me
Customs cannot contain me

I accept me as I am
As I do me, I am proud to be
To sing
To dance
To laugh
To Be Me!

Sit back
Watch me step
Watch me move
Watch me rock
With pride
Because I am who I was made to be

Little girl, big girl
Beautiful girls

I do me
I love me
All of me!

Girls Rock

I Do Me Discussion Guide

1. What is the main idea of *Beautiful Little Girl?*

2. Explain the statement, 'I do me.'

3. What makes you different that other girls?

4. How are you the same as other girls?

5. Why is it important to respect all girls for who they are?

6. What do you like to do? What are you good at doing?

   What do you want to learn? Who can help you learn?

About the Author

©élan Studios

Ama Oforiwaa Aduonum is a nationally recognized playwright and performer whose solo performance of her art piece, *Walking with My Ancestors: Cape Coast Castle* (2019) has won national awards. Ama has a PhD from Florida State University and teaches courses in Black Music and Ethnomusicology. She also directs Ghanaian Drumming and Dance Ensembles and drum circles. She a Queen Mother in Ghana, *responsible for engaging youth as they move towards progress and success.* As a researcher, writer, choreographer, performance artist, a storyteller, and a motivational speaker, Ama is *interested in both knowledge for its own sake and in using knowledge* to address issues in society. Her aim is to motivate others to accept and love themselves and help their communities. Ama enjoys cooking and spending time with her family in her spare time. She lives in the Midwest.

About the Illustrator

Kojo Kisseh Aduonum, a.k.a. Dark Chocolate, is a talented young artist, who has been drawing since he could hold a pencil at 2. He enjoys working with his 2 or 3 favorite mediums to create artwork. Kojo's career goal is to become an airline pilot. He plays mid-field on the soccer team; he also plays trumpet. When he is not drawing, Kojo likes to skateboard, read comic books, listen to music, and play games with his family. He loves playing outside whether it is hot or cold. He loves roaming in the wilderness, when he gets a chance. Kojo lives in the Midwest with his family.

Made in the USA
Coppell, TX
22 August 2021